MAHLER

24 SONGS, v.2

FOR VOICE AND PIANO

(LOW)

VOLUME II

No. 1232

INTERNATIONAL MUSIC COMPANY

509 FIFTH AVENUE   NEW YORK CITY

Printed in U.S.A.

DAS IRDISCHE LEBEN

"Mutter, ach Mutter, es hungert mich.
Gib mir Brod, sonst sterbe ich!"
"Warte nur! Warte nur, mein liebes Kind!
Morgen wollen wir ernten geschwind!"
Und als das Korn geerntet war,
Rief das Kind noch immerdar:
"Mutter, ach Mutter, es hungert mich,
Gib mir Brod, sonst sterbe ich!"
"Warte nur, warte nur, mein liebes Kind,
Morgen wollen wir dreschen geschwind!"
Und als das Korn gedroschen war,
Rief das Kind noch immerdar:
"Mutter, ach Mutter, es hungert mich,
Gib mir Brod, sonst sterbe ich!"
"Warte nur, warte nur, mein Liebes Kind,
Morgen wollen wir backen geschwind!"
Und als das Brod gebacken war,
Lag das Kind auf der Todtenbahr!

THE EARTHLY LIFE

"Mother, oh mother, so hungry am I.
Give me bread, else I shall die!"
"Wait only! Wait only, my dear child!
Tomorrow we shall harvest so fast!"
And when the corn had been harvested,
The child still kept calling unendingly:
"Mother, oh mother, so hungry am I,
Give me bread, else I shall die!"
"Wait only, wait only, my dear child,
Tomorrow we shall thrash so fast!"
And when the corn had been thrashed,
The child still kept calling unendingly:
"Mother, oh mother, so hungry am I,
Give me bread, else I shall die!"
"Wait only, wait only, my dear child,
Tomorrow we shall bake so fast!"
And when the bread had been baked at last,
The child lay on the bier!

UM SCHLIMME KINDER ARTIG ZU MACHEN

Es kam ein Herr zum Schlösseli
Auf einem schönen Rössli,
Ku-ku-kuk, ku-ku-kuk!
Da lugt die Frau zum Fenster aus
Und sagt: "der Mann ist nicht zu Haus,
Und niemand, und niemand,
Und niemand heim als meine Kind',
Und's Mädchen und's Mädchen ist auf der
    Wäschewind!"
Der Herr auf seinem Rössli
Sagt zu der Frau im Schlösseli:
Ku-ku-kuk, ku-ku-kuk!
"Sind's gute Kind', sind's böse Kind'?
Ach, liebe Frau, ach sagt geschwind,"
Ku-ku-kuk, ku-ku-kuk!
"In meiner Tasch' für folgsam Kind',
Da hab' ich manche Angebind,"
Ku-ku-kuk, ku-ku-kuk!
Die Frau die sagt: "sehr böse Kind'!
Sie folgen Muttern nicht geschwind,
Sind böse, sind böse!"
Die Frau, die sagt: "sind böse Kind!
Sie folgen der Mutter nicht geschwind!"
Da sagt der Herr: "so reit' ich heim,
Dergleichen Kinder brauch' ich kein'!"
Ku-ku-kuk, ku-ku-kuk!
Und reit' auf seinem Rössli
Weit, weit entweg vom Schlösseli!
Ku-ku-kuk, ku-ku-kuk!

TO MAKE BAD CHILDREN GOOD

There came a lord to the little castle
On a beautiful little horse.
Cu-cu-ckoo, cu-cu-ckoo!
There looks the lady out of the window
And says: "my husband is not at home,
And nobody, and nobody,
And nobody home except my children,
And the maidservant is in the wash-house!"

The lord on his little horse
Says to the lady in the little castle:
Cu-cu-ckoo, cu-cu-ckoo!
"Are they good children, are they bad children?
Oh, dear lady, oh tell me quickly,"
Cu-cu-ckoo, cu-cu-ckoo!
In my bag for obedient children,
I have many gifts,"
Cu-cu-ckoo, cu-cu-ckoo!
The lady says: "very bad children!
They don't obey their mother quickly,
They are bad, they are bad!"
The lady says: "very bad children!
They don't obey their mother quickly!"
So the lord says: "then I will ride home,
For such children I have no use!"
Cu-cu-ckoo, cu-cu-ckoo!
And he rides on his little horse
Far, far away from the little castle!
Cu-cu-ckoo, cu-cu-ckoo!

ICH GING MIT LUST
DURCH EINEN GRÜNEN WALD

Ich ging mit Lust durch einen grünen Wald,
Ich hört' die Vöglein singen.
Sie sangen so jung, sie sangen so alt,
Die kleinen Waldvögelein im grünen Wald,
Im grünen Wald!
Wie gern' hört' ich sie singen, ja singen!
Nun sing', nun sing', nun sing', Frau Nachtigall!
Sing' du's bei meinem Feinsliebchen:
Komm schier, komm schier, wenn's finster ist,
Wenn niemand auf der Gasse ist,
Dann komm' zu mir, dann komm' zu mir!
Herein will ich dich lassen, ja lassen!
Der Tag verging, die Nacht brach an,
Er kam zu Feinsliebchen, Feinsliebchen gegangen.
Er klopt so leis' wohl an den Ring,
Ei, schläfst du oder wachst, mein Kind?
Ich hab' so lang' gestanden,
Ich hab' so lang' gestanden!
Es schaut der Mond durch's Fensterlein
Zum holden, süssen Lieben,
Die Nachtigall sang die ganze Nacht.
Du schlafselig' Mägdelein,
Nimm dich in Acht, nimm dich in Acht!
Wo ist dein Herzliebster geblieben?

AUS! AUS!

"Heute marschieren wir!
Juch-he, juch-he, im grünen Mai!
Morgen marschieren wir
Zu dem hohen Thor hinaus,
Zum hohen Thor hinaus! Aus!"
"Reis'st du denn schon fort?
Je, je! Mein Liebster!
Kommst niemals wieder heim?
Je! Je! Mein Liebster?"
"Heute marschieren wir,
Juch-he, juch-he, im grünen Mai!
Ei, du schwarzbraun's Mägdelein,
Uns're Lieb' ist noch nicht aus,
Die Lieb' ist noch nicht aus, aus!
Trink' du ein Gläschen Wein
Zur Gesundheit dein und mein!
Siehst du diesen Strauss am Hut?
Jetzo heisst's marschieren gut!
Nimm das Tüchlein aus der Tasch',
Deine Thränlein mit abwasch'!
Heute marschieren wir,
Juch-he, juch-he, im grünen Mai;
Morgen marschieren wir,
Juch-he, im grünen Mai!"
"Ich will in's Kloster geh'n,
Weil mein Schatz davon geht!
Wo geht's denn hin, mein Schatz?
Gehst du fort, heut schon fort?
Und kommst nimmer wieder?
Ach! Wie wird's traurig sein
Hier in dem Städtchen!
Wie bald vergisst du mein!
Ich! Armes Mädchen!"
"Morgen marschieren wir,
Juch-he, juch-he, im grünen Mai!
Tröst dich, mein lieber Schatz,
Im Mai blüh'n gar viel Blümelein!
Die Lieb' ist noch nicht aus!
Aus! Aus! Aus! Aus!"

I WENT JOYFULLY THROUGH
A GREEN WOOD

I went joyfully through a green wood,
I heard the little birds sing.
They sang so young, they sang so old,
The little woodbirds in the green wood,
In the green wood!
How gladly I heard them sing, yes, sing!
Now sing, now sing, now sing, Madam Nightingale!
Sing this to my dear sweetheart:
Come along, come along, when it is dark,
When nobody is about,
Then come to me, then come to me!
I will let you in, yes let you in!
The day went by, the night began,
He came to his sweetheart, his sweetheart.
He taps so softly on the knocker,
Oh, are you asleep or awake, my child?
I have been standing so long,
I have been standing so long!
The moon looks through the window small
At their lovely, sweet embraces,
The nightingale sang all the night.
You sleep-charmed maiden,
Take care, take care!
Where is your dear lover now?

OVER! OVER!

"Today we march!
High ho, high ho, in the green May!
Tomorrow we shall march away
Out of the high gate,
Out of the high gate! Out!"
"Are you already going away?
Oh my, oh my! My dearest!
Won't you ever come back home again?
Oh my! Oh my! My dearest!
"Today we march,
High ho, high ho, in the green May!
Oh you dark brown little maiden,
Our love is not yet over,
Love is not yet over, over!
Drink a little glass of wine
To your health and mine!
Do you see these flowers on my hat?
Now we really have to march!
Take your kerchief from your pouch,
Your little tears to wipe away!
Today we march,
High ho, high ho, in the green May;
Tomorrow we shall march,
High ho, in the green May!"
"I want to go into the convent,
Because my sweetheart is going away!
Where are you going, my sweetheart?
Do you go away, already today?
And will you never come back?
Oh! How sad it will be
Here in the little town!
How soon you will forget me!
Poor maiden I!"
"Tomorrow we shall march,
High ho, high ho, in the green May!
Console yourself, my dear sweetheart,
In May many flowers are blooming!
Love is not yet over!
Over! Over! Over! Over!"

STARKE EINBILDUNGSKRAFT

Hast gesagt, du willst mich nehmen,
So bald der Sommer kommt!
Der Sommer ist gekommen, ja kommen,
Du hast mich nicht genommen, ja nommen!
Geh', Büble, geh'! Geh', nehm' mich!
Geh', Büble, geh'! Geh', nehm' mich!
Gelt, ja? Gelt ja? Gelt ja, du nimmst mich noch?
Wie soll ich dich denn nehmen,
Dieweil ich doch schon hab'?
Und wenn ich halt an dich gedenk',
Und wenn ich halt an dich gedenk',
So mein' ich, so mein ich,
So mein' ich alle weile:
Ich wär' schon bei dir!

STRONG IMAGINATION

You have said you want to take me,
As soon as summer comes!
Summer has come, yes come,
You have not taken me, not taken me!
Look, boy, look! Look here, take me!
Look, boy, look! Look here, take me!
Won't you? Won't you? Won't you take me yet?
How then shall I take you
When I already have you?
And when I just do think of you,
And when I just do think of you,
It seems to me, it seems to me,
It seems to me all the while:
That I were already with you!

WO DIE SCHÖNEN TROMPETEN BLASEN

Wer ist denn draussen und wer klopfet an
Der mich so leise, so leise wecken kann?
Das ist der Herzallerliebste dein,
Steh' auf und lass mich zu dir ein!
Was soll ich hier nun länger steh'n?
Ich seh' di Morgenröth' aufgeh'n,
Die Morgenröth', zwei helle Stern'.
Bei meinem Schatz da wär' ich gern'!
Bei meinem Herzallerliebe!
Das Mädchen stand auf und liess ihn ein,
Sie heisst ihn auch willkommen sein.
Willkommen, lieber Knabe mein!
So lang hast du gestanden!
Sie reicht' ihm auch die schneeweisse Hand.
Von ferne sang die Nachtigall,
Das Mädchen fing zu weinen an.
Ach weine nicht, du Liebste mein,
Ach weine nicht, du Liebste mein!
Auf's Jahr sollst du mein Eigen sein.
Mein Eigen sollst du werden gewiss,
Wie's Keine sonst auf Erden ist!
O Lieb auf grüner Erden.
Ich zieh' in Krieg auf grüne Haid';
Die grüne Haide, die ist so weit!
Allwo dort die schönen Trompeten blasen,

Da ist mein Haus von grünem Rasen!

WHERE THE BEAUTIFUL TRUMPETS SOUND

Who then is outside and who knocks at the door
Who can so softly, so softly wake me?
That is your heart's best-beloved,
Arise and let me come in!
Why should I stand here any longer?
I see the dawn come up,
The dawn, two bright stars.
With my sweetheart I would like to be!
With my heart's best-beloved!
The maiden arose and let him in,
She bids him welcome too.
Welcome, dear boy of mine!
So long you have been standing!
She gives him also her snow-white hand.
From far away sang the nightingale,
The maiden then began to weep.
Oh do not, you love of mine,
Oh do not weep, you love of mine!
Next year you shall be all mine own.
Mine own you shall be for certain,
As no other maid is on earth!
Oh love on the green earth.
I go to war on the green heath;
The green heath, it is so far!
It is there where the beautiful trumpets are
    sounding,
There is my house my house of green turf.

English translation by EDITH BRAUN

Das irdische Leben.

GUSTAV MAHLER
(1860-1911)

6

„„War - te nur!

War - te nur, mein lie - bes__ Kind! Mor - gen wol - len wir

ern - ten ge - schwind!"""

cantabile

Und__ als das Korn__ ge -

1232

8

Mut - ter, ach Mut - ter, es hun - gert mich, gib mir

Brot, sonst ster - be ich!"

„War - te nur, war - te nur, mein lie - bes

Kind! Mor - gen wol - len wir bak - ken ge - schwind!" "

10

Etwas zögernd.
(hesitant)

Und als das Brot ge - bak - ken war,

1232

lag das
Kind auf der To - - - ten - - - bahr!

Um schlimme Kinder artig zu machen.

(Aus: „Des Knaben Wunderhorn.")

Es kam ein Herr zum Schlö-sse-li auf ei-nem schö-nen Röss'-li, ku-ku-kuk, ku-ku-kuk! Da lugt die Frau zum Fen-ster aus und sagt: „der Mann ist nicht zu Haus, und nie-mand, und nie-mand, und

niе-mand heim als mei - ne Kind', und 's Mäd-chen, und 's Mäd-chen ist auf der Wä-schewind!" Der

Herr auf sei - nem Rö - sse-li sagt zu der Frau im Schlö - sse-li: Ku -

mit Ped.

ku - kuk, ku - ku - kuk! „„Sind's gu - te Kind', sind's bö - se Kind? Ach,

lie-be Frau, ach sagt geschwind,"" „ku - ku - kuk, ku - ku - kuk!

*) The lower Octaves in both hands may be omitted in order to facilitate the execution
*) Zur Erleichterung des Spielers kann in beiden Händen die untere Octave weggelassen werden.

Ich ging mit Lust durch einen grünen Wald.

(Aus: „Des Knaben Wunderhorn".)

18

1232

Aus! Aus!

(Aus: „Des Knaben Wunderhorn.")

he, juch-he, im grü-nen Mai! Ei, du schwarzbraun's Mäg-de-lein, un-s're Lieb' ist
noch nicht aus, die Lieb' ist noch nicht aus, aus! Trink' du ein Gläs-chen Wein
zur Ge-sund-heit dein und mein! Siehst du die-sen Strauss am Hut? Je-tzo heisst's mar-
schi-ren gut! Nimm das Tüch-lein aus der Tasch', dei-ne Thrän-lein mit abwasch'!

Starke Einbildungskraft.

(Aus: „Des Knaben Wunderhorn.")

Wo die schönen Trompeten blasen.

lang hast du ge - stan - den!   Sie

reicht' ihm auch die_ schneeweiße Hand.   Von

fer - ne sang_ die Nach - ti - gall, das Mäd - chen fing_ zu wei - -

non legato

- -nen an.   Ach

wei - ne nicht, du Lieb - ste mein, ach wei - ne nicht, du Lieb - ste

mein! Auf's Jahr sollst du mein ei - gen sein.

Mein ei - gen sollst du wer - den ge - wiß, wie's kei - ne sonst auf

Er - den ist! O Lieb auf grü - ner Er - - - -

Various Song Collections

BERLIOZ
Les Nuits d'Eté. A Cycle of Six Songs
  (Fr. & Eng.) High or Low 2.00

BRAHMS
70 Songs. (SERGIUS KAGEN)
  (Ger. & Eng.) High or Low 4.50
42 Folk Songs. (Ger. & Eng.)
  High or Low. Vols. I, II .... Each 2.00
Zigeunerlieder. 8 Songs. (G. & E.) H. or L. 1.25

CHAUSSON
20 Songs (SERGIUS KAGEN) High or Low 3.00
Poème de l'Amour et de la Mer. High 2.00

DEBUSSY
43 Songs (SERGIUS KAGEN) (Fr. & Eng.)
  High or Low-Medium. 4.50

DUPARC
11 Songs. (SERGIUS KAGEN) (Fr. & Eng.)
  High 2.50
12 Songs. (SERGIUS KAGEN) (Fr. & Eng.)
  Medium or Low .... Each 2.50

DVOŘÁK
Gypsy Songs. A Cycle of 7 Songs. English
  version by H. PROCTER-GREGG
  High or Low 1.50
Biblical Songs. A Cycle of 10 Songs. English
  version by H. PROCTER-GREGG
  High or Low. Vols. I, II .... Each 1.25

FAURÉ
30 Songs. (SERGIUS KAGEN) (Fr. & Eng.)
  High, Medium or Low 3.00
La Bonne Chanson. 9 Songs. (Fr. & Eng.)
  High or Low. 1.75

FORTY FRENCH SONGS
Selected and edited by SERGIUS KAGEN
High, Medium or Low. Vols. I, II ...... Each 3.00

GRANADOS
11 Songs (Tonadillas) (Span. & Eng.) 2.00

HAHN
12 Songs. (SERGIUS KAGEN). High 2.25
10 Songs. (SERGIUS KAGEN) Low. 1.75

HANDEL
45 Arias from Operas and Oratorios.
  (SERGIUS KAGEN). High or Low
  Vols. I, II, III .... Each 2.50

ITALIAN SONGS OF THE 18th CENTURY
Album of 20 Songs. (FUCHS).
(Ital. & Eng.) Medium 2.50

MAHLER
24 Songs. (Ger. & Eng.) High or Low
  Vols. I, II, III, IV. .... Each 1.75
Kindertotenlieder. Medium-Low 1.75
Lieder eines fahrenden Gesellen (Songs
  of a Wayfarer). (Ger. & Eng.) 1.75

MOZART
Arias from Operas. (Many not heretofore
available). Original texts with English
translations. (SERGIUS KAGEN)
For Soprano. Vols. I, II, III, IV .... Each 2.50
For Coloratura Soprano. 10 Arias 2.50
For Contralto. 7 Arias 2.50
For Tenor. Vol. I 2.50
For Bass or Baritone. 20 Arias. Vols. I, II. Each 2.50
For Bass. 10 Arias. 2.50

MUSSORGSKY
Songs and Dances of Death. A Cycle of 4
  Songs. (English adaptation by MARION
  FARQUHAR.) (Russ. & Eng.)
  High, Medium or Low 2.00
Without Sun. A Cycle of Six Songs. English
  version by H. PROCTER-GREGG
  (Russ. & Eng.) Medium-Low 2.00
The Nursery. A Cycle of 7 Songs. (SERGIUS
  KAGEN). Original key 2.00

OBRADORS
Classical Spanish Songs. (Span. & Eng.) Med. 2.00

PURCELL
40 Songs. Realization of the Figured Bass
  and editing by SERGIUS KAGEN.
  High or Low. Vols. I, II, III, IV ...... Each 2.50
6 Songs for Bass. (SERGIUS KAGEN) 2.00
4 Sacred Songs. (from 'Harmonia Sacra')
  (SERGIUS KAGEN). High or Low. 2.00

RAVEL
3 Songs (Fr. & Eng.) 1.00
5 Greek Folk Songs. (Fr. Grk. & Eng.) 2.00
4 Folk Songs. (Fr. & Eng.) (Med.) New 1.50
  English version by H. PROCTER-GREGG
Sheherazade. (Fr. & Eng.) High 2.00

SCHUBERT
200 Songs. (SERGIUS KAGEN) (Ger. & Eng.)
  High or Low. In 3 Volumes. Vol. I 5.00
  Vols. II, III .... Each 4.00

SCHUMANN
85 Songs. (SERGIUS KAGEN)
  (Ger. & Eng.) High 4.50
90 Songs. (SERGIUS KAGEN)
  (Ger. & Eng.) Low 4.50

STRAUSS
30 Songs. (SERGIUS KAGEN) High 3.50
27 Songs. (SERGIUS KAGEN)
  (Ger. & Eng.) Medium or Low .... Each 3.00

SUBIRA
Classical Spanish Songs (12) (Span. & Eng.) 2.00

VIVALDI
4 Arias. (TURCHI) High 1.50

WOLF
65 Songs. (SERGIUS KAGEN)
  (Ger. & Eng.) High or Low 4.50

INTERNATIONAL MUSIC COMPANY

No. 25-64   509 Fifth Avenue   New York 17, N. Y.